FRANCINE PASCAL'S
SWEET VALLEY
Twins

NICOLE ANDELFINGER • CLAUDIA AGUIRRE

Jump into this exclusive sneak preview of *Sweet Valley Twins: Teacher's Pet*, packed with bonus content!

Created and story by FRANCINE PASCAL
Adaptaion written by NICOLE ANDELFINGER
Illustrated by CLAUDIA AGUIRRE
Colors by SARA HAGSTROM
Letters by WARREN MONTGOMERY

Text copyright © 2023 by Francine Pascal
Cover art and interior illustrations copyright © 2023 by Claudia Aguirre

All rights reserved. Published in the United States by RH Graphic, an imprint of Random House Children's Books, a division of Penguin Random House LLC, New York.

RH Graphic with the book design is a trademark of Penguin Random House LLC.

Visit us on the web! RHKidsGraphic.com • @RHKidsGraphic

Educators and librarians, for a variety of teaching tools, visit us at RHTeachersLibrarians.com

Library of Congress Cataloging-in-Publication Data is available upon request.
ISBN 978-0-593-37650-8 (trade paperback) — ISBN 978-0-593-37651-5 (hardcover)
ISBN 978-0-593-37652-2 (library binding) — ISBN 978-0-593-37653-9 (ebook)

Designed by Patrick Crotty

Printed in the United States of America

A comic on every bookshelf.

FREE COMIC BOOK DAY™

FRANCINE PASCAL'S
SWEET VALLEY
Twins
THE GRAPHIC NOVEL

NICOLE ANDELFINGER • CLAUDIA AGUIRRE

**EXCLUSIVE
EXCERPT FROM
TEACHER'S PET,
POSTER, AND
ACTIVITIES INSIDE!**

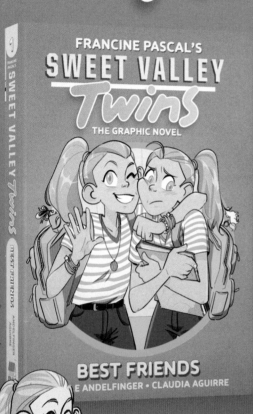

I mean, the beach is a public space! Bruce and his friends could just *happen* to be there. It's a free country!

It's California-- every day is beach weather. But there's the big recital, and you've only got one chance at the lead.

Like I have a chance anyway. Everyone knows you're Madame André's favorite. You could just not show up and *still* get the lead.

Jessica, Madame André would never play favorites like that! Everyone has an equal chance at the solo, including you.

Definitely Elizabeth. Madame is always complimenting her.

No more than anyone else!

Okay, but I'm pretty sure--

I think it will be Elizabeth too.

Definitely. I'm mostly hoping for one of the minor parts at this point!

I'm sure Madame André will choose whoever is best for the part!

Yeah, and that *who* is *you!*

Can I try on the tiara when you get the part? Just once?

Maybe you can try it on...in exchange for your quote for the recital program!

That's right-- you and Amy are making the program for the recital?

Yup! We want to make sure everyone gets a chance to shine--

--so be sure to give us a quote about what dance means to you. It's going to be great, right, Amy?

It's gonna be good, promise! We just need the quote the night before the recital.

A great dancer *and* a great writer. What can't you do, Elizabeth?

As most of you are aware, auditions for the feature piece of our recital are soon.

I will announce more about the piece at the end of class.

I also want to remind you all to practice hard and practice often, particularly outside of class.

A great dancer must practice more than the two hours a week I see you.

Now, let us begin.

First position at the barre, *s'il vous plaît!*

Poster Illustration by Claudia Aguirre
Poster Colors by Janet Sung

Before we end, I wish to talk more about the upcoming recital...

As you know, this year the studio will hold a fall recital in the Sweet Valley High School auditorium. This class has been given the honor of performing last.

You have all grown as dancers, which is why I wish to showcase your talents with a timeless, beautiful, technical classic--

Is it *The Nutcracker?*

Non, non! A classic, yes, but perhaps something to look forward to in next year's class!

No, we will be performing a piece from a classic, comedic, *romantic* ballet: *Coppélia.*

Romantic... That means love!

What is it about, Madame André?

Everyone, practice! Remember...

...only the most dedicated of dancer will be given a chance to shine in the lead!

Oh, you're home! How was class?

Ugh.

Mom! Mom!

Auditions for the recital are in a week, and Madame André is going to choose five dancers. Four get minor roles and one person gets to be the lead, Swanilda. Everyone has a chance to dance for the parts.

Isn't it exciting, Jessica?

Turn the page for bonus activities!

JESSICA AND ELIZABETH'S FRIENDSHIP TIME CAPSULE!

When you have a great BFF, making amazing memories is super easy! Save these moments for your future selves with the help of a friendship time capsule! Here's how to get started.

1. With your BFF, find any big container, like a shoebox or large jar, and decorate the outside! Get creative with the materials—you can use glitter, magazine clippings, or paint. Make sure to also label it with your names and the date you plan to open it!

2. Once your time capsule is ready, find items that symbolize your friendship. Here are some ideas of what you can include:

    • A printed picture of you and your BFF

    • A list of fun things you enjoy doing together

    • Letters to your future selves

    • Friendship bracelets, tickets, or other keepsakes

3. Now that your time capsule is packed full of memories, all that's left to do is find a good place to keep it!

Whether you're having a sleepover with your BFFs or chilling with your siblings, use these activities to make any time a blast!

BFF QUIZ!

How well do you and your BFF know each other? On separate sheets of paper, write down how you think your friend or sibling would answer. Read your answers aloud to see if you were right!

1. What is my favorite movie?

2. If I had to eat ONE thing for the rest of my life, what would it be?

3. Would I rather dye my hair neon or roller-skate everywhere I went?

4. What is my favorite hobby?

5. What is something I couldn't live without?

6. What is my favorite city to visit?

7. If I could be anything in the world, what would I be?

8. What is my favorite song right now?

9. Would I rather go on a hike or chill by the pool?

10. What is our funniest friendship moment?

TBR PERSONALITY QUIZ!

What should be next on your TBR (to be read) list?
Take this personality quiz to discover which
graphic novel belongs on your shelf!

START HERE!

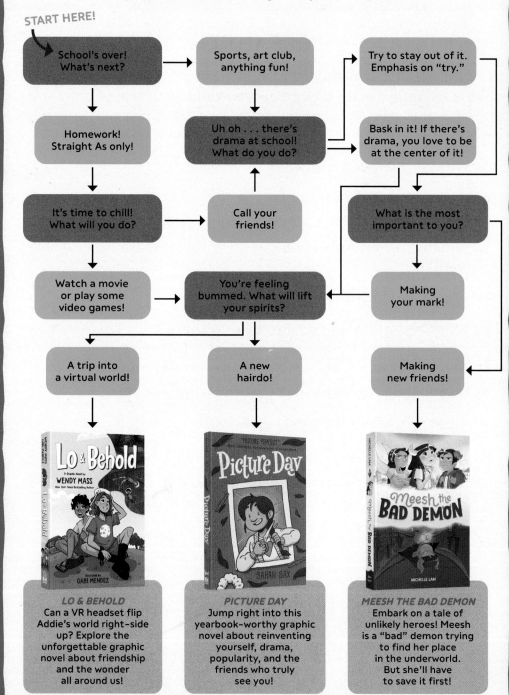

School's over! What's next! → Sports, art club, anything fun! → Try to stay out of it. Emphasis on "try."

Homework! Straight As only!

Uh oh . . . there's drama at school! What do you do?

Bask in it! If there's drama, you love to be at the center of it!

It's time to chill! What will you do? → Call your friends!

What is the most important to you?

Watch a movie or play some video games! → You're feeling bummed. What will lift your spirits?

Making your mark!

A trip into a virtual world!

A new hairdo!

Making new friends!

LO & BEHOLD
Can a VR headset flip Addie's world right-side up? Explore the unforgettable graphic novel about friendship and the wonder all around us!

PICTURE DAY
Jump right into this yearbook-worthy graphic novel about reinventing yourself, drama, popularity, and the friends who truly see you!

MEESH THE BAD DEMON
Embark on a tale of unlikely heroes! Meesh is a "bad" demon trying to find her place in the underworld. But she'll have to save it first!

YOUR 2023 GRAPHIC NOVEL
CHECKLIST!

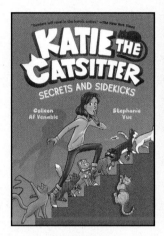

☐

☐

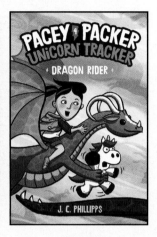

☐

☐

☐

☐

LOVE GRAPHIC NOVELS?
CHECK OUT THESE EXCITING NEW READS!

Art (from top to bottom): © 2023 by Gabi Mendez; © 2023 by Sarah Sax; © 2023 by Michelle Lam

WILL ELIZABETH TAKE THE LEAD, OR WILL JESSICA'S JEALOUSY TAKE CENTER STAGE?

Get ready for an exclusive sneak peek into the all-new SWEET VALLEY TWINS: TEACHER'S PET! Jessica knows she's the better dancer—but their teacher only seems to have eyes for her sister Elizabeth! With Jessica's attitude rapidly souring and Elizabeth slowly realizing that Jessica might actually be right, will they be able to find a way to get Jessica her leading role?

BONUS!
Features an exclusive Sweet Valley Twins poster and activities to share with friends!

FRANCINE PASCAL'S

SWEET VALLEY

Twins

THE GRAPHIC NOVEL

BEST FRIENDS

NICOLE ANDELFINGER • CLAUDIA AGUIRRE

Art © 2023 by Claudia Aguirre

Don't miss the first
SWEET VALLEY
Twins
graphic novel!

Follow us @randomhousekids 📷 🐦

ISBN 978-0-593-70725-8

9 780593 707258